KID
-O-
JOKES

This edition published in 2010 by

Wilco
Publishing House
Mumbai 400 023. India
Tel: 22041420 / 22842574 Fax: (91-22) 22041429
E mail: wilcos@vsnl.com

ISBN 978-81-88280-82-8

Printed in India

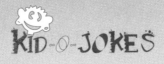

Three boys called Manners, Shut up and Trouble were playing in the woods one day, when Trouble suddenly vanished from sight! Try as they would, Shut up and Manners were unable to find him; they ran and shouted and ran and shouted, but Trouble had managed to get himself totally lost. So Shut up and Manner decided to go and report Trouble's disappearance to the police. When they arrived at the police station, Manners waited outside on the steps while Shut up went in.

"What's your name, sonny?" asked the policeman behind the inquiries desk.

"Shut up," replied the boy.

"Eh?" said the policeman, startled,"Where are your manners?"

"Sitting outside on the steps," replied Shut up.

The policeman's brow darkened. "Are you looking for trouble?" he scowled.

"Yes," said Shut up, "how did you know?"

**********  **********

Q: If you peel my skin off, I won't cry, but you will. What am I?
A: An onion.

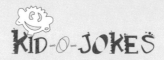

KID-O-JOKES

Knock Knock!
Who's there?
Amos.
Amos who?
A mosquito just bit me!

********* **********

Q: What has four legs one head but only one foot?
A: A bed

********* **********

One day two girls were late for school. When one of the girls walked into the classroom, the teacher asked, "Where were you?"
The girl replied, "I was at the lake throwing pebbles."
A few minutes later, the second girl walked in the room. The teacher asked her the same thing. The girl said the same thing. A few minutes later, a new girl that was dripping wet walked in the room.
The teacher asked, "Hello, what is your name?"
The girl replied, "My name is Pebbles."

A man went scuba diving. He went 10 feet into the water and he saw a man that was also in the same level of water but with no scuba gear. He went another 30 feet and noticed the same man again.
So he pulled out his waterproof chalkboard and wrote: "How are you diving without your scuba gear?"
The man snatched the waterproof chalkboard and wrote: "I'm drowning, you fool!"

********* 🙂 *********

Knock-knock.
Who's there?
Wire.
Wire who?
Wire you asking me?

********* 🙂 *********

Q: Where do cows go to have fun?
A: To the mooovies!

********* 🙂 *********

Knock Knock
Who's there?
Les
Les who?
Les go for a swim!

Knock Knock
Who's there?
Justin
Justin who?
Justin time for supper!

*********  **********

My sister came home and said, "Mum, can I have a
pair of shoes for gym?"
My mum said, "Tell him to get his own shoes!"

********* :) **********

Q: Why didn't the skeleton go to the ball?
A: Because he had no body to go with!

********* :) **********

Knock Knock
who's there
Madeja
Madeja who ?
Madja open the door

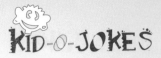

KID-O-JOKES

Once there were four aliens and they came to Earth. They could only say one phrase in English. The first one went to an opera and learned how to say: "Me, me, me." The second one went to a restaurant and learned how to say: "With knives and forks." The third one went to a candy store and learned how to say: "Because he stole my lollipop." The fourth one went to a baseball game and learned how to say: "Yeah, yeah, yeah." One day there was a dead man on the road, the policeman pulled the aliens over and said, "Who killed this man?" The first alien said, "Me, me, me." The policeman said, "How did you kill him?" The second alien said, "With knives and forks, with knives and forks." The policeman said, "Why did you kill him?" The third alien said, "Because he stole my lollipop." The policeman said, "You're going to jail." The fourth alien said, "Yeah, yeah, yeah!"

********* ☺ **********

Knock Knock
Who's there?
Sarah
Sarah who?
Sarah doctor in the house?

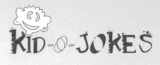

KID-O-JOKES

There was once a man from Peru,
Who dreamt he was eating his shoe.
He woke up in a fright,
In the middle of the night
And found it was perfectly true.

*********  **********

Q: Why is a cat in the desert like Christmas?
A: Because of its sandy claws!

*********  **********

Son: I can't go to school today.
Father: Why not?
Son: I don't feel well.
Father: Where don't you feel well?
Son: In school!

********* **********

Knock! Knock!
Who's there?
Winnie the!
Winnie the who?
No. Not Winnie the who! Winnie the Pooh!

Knock Knock
Who's there?
Boo
Boo who?
Stop crying, it's just a joke!

*********  **********

Q: What notes does the tightrope-musician have to
worry about?
A: C sharp or B flat!

*********  **********

Kathy: I feel sorry for my math book.
Peter: Why?
Kathy: Because it has so many problems.

********* **********

Knock Lnock
Who's there?
Moose.
Moose who?
Moose you be so nosy?

KID-O-JOKES

Knock Knock
Who's there?
Obie
Obie who?
Oh be quiet & open the door.

*********  **********

Q: Why did the chicken cross the road?
A: To show the armadillo it could be done!

********* **********

Doctor: You need new glasses.
Patient: How do you know?
I haven't told you what's wrong with me yet.
Doctor: I could tell as soon as you walked
in through the window!

********* **********

"Did you hear about Cinderella being thrown out of her
school net ball team?"
"No, why was that?"
"Because she kept running away from the ball."

KID-O-JOKES

Once there was an Irish man, a Japanese man and an American man and they were travelling across the desert on donkeys. The Irish man brought wine, the Japanese man brought bread and the American man brought a car door. Another person that was travelling across the desert came and asked them why they had all these things. The Irish man said that he brought the wine in case he got thirsty. The Japanese man said he brought bread in case he got hungry. The American man said, "I brought the car door in case I get hot." The other traveller said, "What do you mean?" Then the American said, "If I get hot, I can roll down the window."

*********  **********

Knock Knock
Who's there?
Olive
Olive who?
Olive You!

*********  **********

Q: Why was 6 afraid of 7?
A: Because 7 8 9!

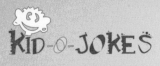

KID-O-JOKES

Why did the chicken cross the road?
Why?
To get the Martian newspaper.
I don't get it.
Neither do I. I can't read Martian.

*********  **********

Q: Why won't cannibals eat clowns?
A: Because they taste funny!

********* **********

Knock Knock
Who's there?
House
House who?
House it going?

********* **********

Q: What do you call a cow in an earthquake?
A: A milkshake!

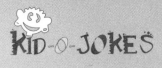

KID-O-JOKES

Knock Knock
Who's there?
Eileen
Eileen who?
Eileen over to tie my shoe!

********* 🙂 **********

Q: What did the porcupine say to the cactus?
A: "Is that you, Mama?"

********* 🙂 **********

Once there were three tomatoes. They were a family. The big one was named Papa, the medium one was named Mama and the little one was named Baby Tomato. They went for a walk and Baby Tomato couldn't catch up so Papa tomato went to the little one and squeezed him and said, "Ketchup."

There was once a lady who was sleeping when she smelt smoke and realised there was a fire in her house. So she rang up the fire brigade and said, "There is a fire in my house."
After she had given them most of the information they asked, "How do we get there?"
Then the lady said, "Er, in your big red fire engine."

*********  **********

Knock Knock
Who's there?
Harry
Harry Who?
Harry Up and open this door

********* **********

Q: What is black and white and sleeps a lot?
A: A snoozepaper!

Q: Why did the chicken cross the road?
A: He didn't want to go to the barbecue!

********** 😊 **********

There was an American man and a Chinese
man lost in the woods. They were hungry so
the Chinese man went looking for food. He
came back with a ton of
food and the American guy asked him how
he did it and he said, "Find track, follow
track, find food."
So the American tried it and came back with
bruises and broken bones.
The Chinese guy asked him what happened
and he said,"Found track, followed track,
got hit by train!"

********** 😊 **********

Knock Knock
Who's there?
Ben
Ben who?
Ben knocking on your door all afternoon!

Knock Knock
Who's there?
Woody.
Woody who?
Woody you want!!

*********  **********

One day a man walked into an empty bar and sat down
next to a bowl of peanuts. All of a sudden he heard
a little voice say, "You have a nice tie."
The man looked around the room but still, nobody was
there except the bartender, who was in the storage room.
He ate a couple of peanuts and again he heard a
little voice say, "Nice hat."
Then he got up to get a drink. When he sat down the
little voice said, "Nice shirt."
The man got very irritated and called the bartender.
He said, "I keep hearing voices but nobody else is here."
The bartender replied, "It's the peanuts.
They're complimentary."

********* 🙂 **********

Q: What did one plate say to the other plate?
A: "Lunch is on me!"

Knock Knock
Who's there?
Banana.
Banana who?
Knock Knock
Who's there?
Banana.
Banana who?
Knock Knock
Who's there?
Orange.
Orange who?
Orange you glad I didn't say banana?

********* 😊 **********

Q: What is black and white and red all over?
A: A sunburnt zebra!

********* 😊 **********

Fred: What's the second to the last letter in the alphabet?
Joe: Y.
Frank: Because I want to know.

A lady stopped at a gas station to refill the gas tank
in her car. She got out and started to fill it.
Suddenly an alien spaceship landed. The alien got out.
The lady saw the letters U.F.O. printed on the side
of the spaceship. The lady asked the alien if U.F.O.
stood for unidentified flying object.
"No," the alien replied,
"it stands for Unleaded Fuel Only."

*********  **********

Q: What happened when the cow jumped over the barbed
wire fence?
A: It was an udder catastrophe!

********* **********

Knock Knock!
Who's there?
Dwayne!
Dwayne who?
Dwayne the bathtub, I'm drowning!

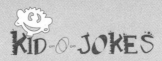

KID-O-JOKES

Knock Knock!
Who's there?
Hutch.
Hutch who?
Oops, I'm out of Kleenex!

********* :) **********

Man: "Lord, what is a thousand years to you?"
God: "A second."
Man: "What is a thousand dollars to you?"
God: "A penny."
Man: "Lord, can I have a penny?"
God: "Yes, just a second."

********* :) **********

Q: What do birds need when they are sick?
A: A tweetment!

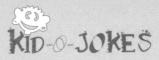 KID-O-JOKES

Q: What do you call a sheep with no legs?
A: A cloud!

*********  **********

One day Stupid Sam (who was very, very stupid)
walked into the barber shop wearing some headphones.
He told the barber he wanted a haircut but he could
not take off the headphones or he would die.
The barber said okay and started to cut his hair,
but the headphones kept getting in the way.
Finally the barber just ripped off the headphones
and threw them across the room.
Stupid Sam fell out of the chair and died.
The barber thought, 'Wow he was serious about that!'
He went over to the headphones and listened to
what was on them. It was a voice saying,
"breathe in, breathe out,
breathe in, breathe out."

*********  **********

Knock, Knock
Who's there?
Evan.
Evan who?
Evan help us if we swallow school cafeteria food.

KID-O-JOKES

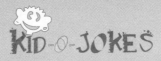

Q: What vegetable do you get when King Kong walks through your garden?
A: Squash!

********* :) *********

Customer: This soup tastes funny..
Waitress: Then why don't you laugh.

********* :) *********

Knock Knock!
Who's there?
Dishes
Dishes who?
Dishes a very bad joke..!!!

********* :) *********

I didn't come here to be insulted...
Why, where do you usually go?

21

Once there were three men in an airplane who were very mad at their home states for making them pay high taxes. The first man who was a New Yorker threw a knife. When he landed he saw a little girl who told him that a knife had cut the main power line, so New York had no electricity.

The next man threw locusts and other plant eating insects on Oklahoma's farmland. He found later that half of the state's agriculture had been eaten.

Finally, the third man threw a bomb at the Sears Tower in Illinois. He landed and saw a boy laughing. The boy said that he guzzled down some soda, burped and the Sears Tower exploded.

*********  *********

Knock Knock
Who's there ?
Who
Who Who?
What Are you..... an Owl?

********* :) *********

Q: What did one toilet say to the other toilet?
A: You look a bit flushed!

KID-O-JOKES

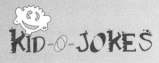

Did you know that I used to be a tap dancer...
but I had to quit
because I kept falling into the sink.

********* :) *********

Knock Knock!
Who's there?
Tish
Tish who?
Bless you!

********* :) *********

Q: What dog keeps the best time?
A: A watch dog.

********* :) *********

Knock Knock
Who's there ?
Cheese
Cheese Who ?
Cheese it's cold out here

KID-O-JOKES

Q: What do you get when you cross a telephone
with a very big football player?
A: A wide receiver!

********* 🙂 **********

Once upon a time there was a worm with 100 feet
called Tom. One day he and his friend were chased
by a chicken .Tom quickly got into his house
but his friend was trapped outside and told Tom,
"Please let me in."
Tom answered, "After I put on my shoes."

********* 🙂 **********

Knock Knock
Who's there?
Madam
Madam who?
Madam foot got stuck in the door

KID-O-JOKES

Q: Why did the man destroy his piano?
A: He was looking for his keys!

********* 😊 **********

Knock Knock
Who's there?
Interrupting Cow
Interrupting Cow who..............
MOOOO

********* 😊 **********

Once there were two house painters, and one was on a
ladder. "Have you got a good firm grip on your brush?"
yelled the one down below.
"Yep" the one on the ladder called.
"O.K. then hang on to the brush,
because I need the ladder."

********* 😊 **********

Doctor, Doctor, I can't get to sleep.
Sit on the edge of the bed and you'll soon drop off.

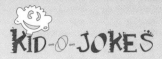

Dilly: What has two horns and goes "oom, oom"?
Dally: A cow walking backwards.

********* 🙂 **********

Knock Knock
Who's there?
Orange
Orange who?
Orange you tired of these knock knock jokes?

********* 🙂 **********

Doctor, Doctor, I feel like a bell.
Take these pills, and if they don't help, give me a ring.

********* 🙂 **********

Q: What do you call a 5000 pound gorilla?
A: Sir!

KID-O-JOKES

Once there was a man named Sam and he didn't have the patience to sit and wait. So one day an old man came along and said to him,
"I guess you'll never become a doctor."
"Why?" Sam asked.
The man said, "because you don't have any patience."

*********  *********

Knock Knock
Who's there?
Howdy!
Howdy who?
Howdy do that?

*********  *********

Q: Why don't elephants smoke?
A: They can't fit their 'butts' in the ashtray!

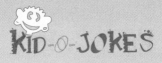

There were three men who found a magic lamp.
The genie came out and gave them each a wish.
The first man wished to go to his family in France.
The second man wished to see his family in Germany.
The third man said, "I miss my friends,
I wish they would come back."

********* ☺ **********

Knock Knock!
Who's there?
Doughnut
Doughnut who?
Doughnut open until Christmas...!!!

********* ☺ **********

Q: Why did Piglet look in the toilet?
A: He was looking for Pooh.

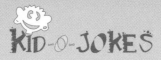

Doctor, Doctor, I feel like a pack of cards.
I'll deal with you later.

********* 🙂 *********

Doctor, Doctor, I feel like a spoon.
Sit still and don't stir.

********* 🙂 *********

Knock Knock!
Who's there?
Leaf
Leaf who?
Leaf me alone

********* 🙂 *********

Q: Why do cows use the doorbell?
A: Because their horns don't work!

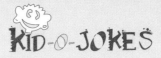

KID-O-JOKES

"Mum, can I have 10 p for being good?"
"All right, but I wish you could be good-for-nothing!"

********* 🙂 **********

Knock Knock
Who's there?
Little ole lady
Little ole lady who?
I never knew you could yodel !!

********* 🙂 **********

Q: Why did the turkey cross the road?
A: It was the chicken's day off!!!

********* 🙂 **********

Doctor, Doctor, everyone keeps ignoring me.
Next please!

KID-O-JOKES

A little boy stops in front of a church with his bike
and he sees the priest come out. The priest says,
"Come inside, I want to show you something."
The little boy says to the priest,
"but somebody will steal my bike."
The priest says to him,
"don't worry, the Holy Spirit will watch it."
So the little boy goes inside and the priest says,
"let me show you how to do the sign of the cross.
In the name of the Father, the Son
and the Holy Spirit, Amen. Now you try it."
So the boy says,
"In the name of the Father and the Son, Amen."
The priest says, "What happened to the Holy Spirit?"
The boy replied, "He's outside, watching my bike".

*********  **********

Knock Knock
Who's there ?
Butcher
Butcher who?
Butcher little arms around me!

*********  **********

Q: What do you have if you have 100 rabbits in a row
and 99 step back?
A: A receding hare line!

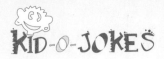

Once upon a time there was a pastor. He was driving
down the road and his car broke down. He got out and
started walking. Soon, he came to a farm. He asked
the farmer if he could borrow a horse.
The farmer agreed, but warned:
"Sir, but this isn't no ordinary horse. You have
to say "praise the Lord" to make it go, and
"Amen" to make it stop".
The pastor said "Oh, that's easy, I'm a pastor.
So he jumped on the horse and said "Praise the Lord!"
and the horse took off down the road.
About an hour down the road (close to his destination),
a rattlesnake came out in front of the horse, and
the horse, rather startled turned and ran off
the road, through the woods, straight for a cliff.
The pastor forgot what to say, so he said a prayer,
and at the end of the prayer, of course,
he said "Amen". Screech!!
The horse stopped right at the edge of the cliff!
The pastor looked down and sees all of the
thousands of feet down that he had almost plundered...
and to give thanks to God, he yelled out
"Praise the Lord!!!!"

**********  **********

Q: Why did the skeleton play the piano?
A: Because he didn`t have any organs!

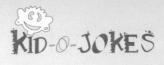

There were three rich men: a Canadian, a Russian and an American. They all wanted to show off to each other so they each bought a toilet. The Russian bought a wooden toilet, the Canadian bought a marble toilet, and the American bought a musical toilet.
The next day the Canadian came back to complain and said, "I want a refund. Every time I use the toilet, I slip off it." The day after that the Russian came to complain and said, "I want a refund. Every time I sit on the toilet I get splinters in my bottom."
The next day, the American came and said, "I want a refund. Every time I sit down, I hear my national anthem and I have to stand up."

********* 😊 *********

Knock Knock
Who's there?
Minnie
Minnie Who?
Minnie people out here freezing.
OPEN THE DOOR!!

********* 😊 *********

Q: What time is it when an elephant sits on a fence?
A: Time to get a new fence!

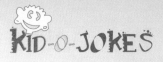

Once upon a time, there was a policeman that saw a man
sitting in a car with a tiger sitting next to him.
The police officer said,
"It's against the law to have a tiger in your car.
Take him to the zoo."
The next day the police officer saw the same man
in the same car with the same tiger.
The police officer said, "I thought I told you
to take that tiger to the zoo."
The man replied, "I did. He liked it.
Now we're going to the beach."

*********  *********

Knock Knock
Who's There?
Ida
Ida Who?
Ida think you'd be tired of these jokes by now!

********* *********

Q: How do you stop a baby alien from crying?
A: You rocket!

KID-O-JOKES

Teacher: What is a comet?
Annie: A star with a tail.
Teacher: Good. Can you name one?
Annie: Lassie!

*********  **********

Knock Knock
Who's there?
Boo
Boo Who?
Dont cry, it's only a joke

*********  **********

Q: Why did the tomato blush?
A: Because it saw the salad dressing!

On a plane were a scientist, a boy scout, a priest,
and the pilot. The pilot comes on the intercom and says,
"We've lost total control of the plane.
There are three parachutes, and I'm taking one."
That left them with two parachutes.
The scientist says, "I'm the smartest man.
What I have to give can save the world!"
So he takes one and jumps.
The priest says, "Son, I'm old and about to die.
Take the parachute."
The boy scout says, "But Father, we can both have one.
The world's smartest man just jumped off the
plane with my back pack."

*********  **********

Knock Knock
Who's there?
Weirdo
Weirdo who?
Weirdo you think you're going?

*********  **********

Q: Why do elephant tusks stick out?
A: Because their parents can`t afford braces!

KID-O-JOKES

Sam : Do you eat with your right hand or left hand.
Mary : Right hand.
Sam : That's strange, I use a fork!

*********  **********

Knock Knock
who's there?
Danielle
Danielle who?
Danielle so loud, I can hear you!

********* **********

Knock Knock
who's there?
easter
easter who?
easter bunny

********* **********

Q: Why did the gum cross the road?
A: Because it was stuck to the chicken!

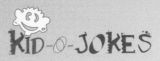

Teacher: "John, go to the map and show us where
North America is."
John: "It is right here."
Teacher: "Correct. Now, class,
who discovered North America?"
Class: "John!"

********* 🙂 *********

Knock Knock
Whos there ?
Harry
Harry who?
Harry up and let me in!!!!

********* 🙂 *********

Q: What did the grape do when it got stepped on?
A: It let out a little wine!

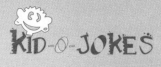

KID-O-JOKES

Gina: 'Dont be afraid of my dog.
You know the old proverb: A barking dog never bites.
Gavin: "You know it and I know it,
but does your dog know it?"

*********  **********

Knock Knock
Whos there ?
Tim
Tim who?
Tim my surprise your still reading these jokes!!!!!

*********  **********

Q: What runs around the yard but does not move?
A: A fence.

********* **********

Q: Why did the Turtle cross the road?
A: To get to the Shell station!

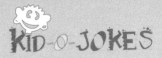

A man goes into a pet shop and tells the owner that he wants to buy a pet that can do everything.

The shop owner suggests a faithful dog. The man replies, "Come on, a dog?"

The owner says, "How about a cat?" The man replies, "No way! A cat certainly can`t do everything. I want a pet that can do everything!" The shop owner thinks for a minute, then says, "I`ve got it! A centipede!"

The man says, "A centipede?

I can`t imagine a centipede doing everything, but okay... I`ll try a centipede."

He gets the centipede home and says to the centipede, "Clean the kitchen." Thirty minutes later, he walks into the kitchen and... it`s immaculate! All the dishes and silverware have been washed, dried, and put away; the counter-tops cleaned; the appliances sparkling the floor waxed.

He`s absolutely amazed. He says to the centipede, "Go clean the living room." Twenty minutes later, he walks into the living room. The carpet has been vacuumed; the furniture cleaned and dusted; the pillows on the sofa plumped; plants watered. The man thinks to himself, "This is the most amazing thing I`ve ever seen. This really is a pet that can do everything!"

Next he says to the centipede, "Run down to the corner and get me a newspaper." The centipede walks out the door. 10 minutes later... no centipede. 20 minutes later... no centipede. 30 minutes later... no centipede.

By this point the man is wondering what`s going on. The centipede should have been back in a couple of minutes. 45 minutes later... still no centipede! He can`t imagine what could have happened. Did the centipede run away? Did it get run over by a car? Where is that centipede?

So he goes to the front door, opens it ... and there`s the centipede sitting right outside.

The man says, "Hey!!! I sent you down to the corner store 45 minutes ago to get me a newspaper. What`s the matter?!!"

The centipede says, "I`m goin`! I`m goin`! I`m just puttin` on my shoes!"

Jimmy: 'Sir, should someone be punished
for something they haven't done?'
Teacher: 'No, of course not.'
Jimmy: 'Good, because I haven't done my homework.'

*********  **********

Knock Knock
Whos there ?
oscar
oscar who ?
oscar silly question, you'll get a silly answer

*********  **********

Q: What do you call a Fairy that doesn't take baths?
A: Stinkerbell!

KID-O-JOKES

Amy: Can people predict the future with cards?
Joan: My mother can.
Amy: Really?
Joan: Yes, she takes one look at my report card and
tells me what will happen when my father gets home.

*********  *********

Knock Knock
Who's there?
Winner
Winner who?
Winner you gonna get this door fixed?

********* *********

Q: Why did the skeleton cross the road?
A: To get to the body shop!

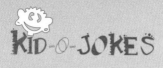

Two morons were working on a house.
The one who was nailing down siding would reach
into his nail pouch, pull out a nail and either toss it
over his shoulder or nail it in.
The other nut, figuring this was worth looking into,
asked, "Why are you throwing those nails away?"
The first explained, "If I pull a nail out of my pouch
and it's pointed TOWARD me, I throw it away
'cause it's defective.
If it's pointed toward the HOUSE, then I nail it in!"
The second got completely upset and yelled,
"You MORON!!!
The nails pointed toward you aren't defective!
They're for the OTHER side of the house!!"

*********  **********

Knock Knock
Whos there ?
Canoe
Canoe who?
Canoe come out to play?

********* :) **********

Q: Why did the chicken cross the park?
A: To get to the other slide!

KID-O-JOKES

TEACHER: How old were you on your last birthday?
STUDENT: Seven.
TEACHER: How old will you be on your next birthday?
STUDENT: Nine.
TEACHER: That's impossible.
STUDENT: No, it isn't, Teacher. I'm eight today.

*********  **********

Knock Knock
Whos there ?
Radio
Radio Who ?
Radio not , here I come !

********* :) **********

Q: What do you call a camel with three humps?
A: Humphrey!

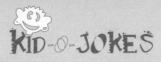
KID-O-JOKES

TEACHER: Willy, name one important thing we have
today that we didn't have ten years ago.
WILLY: Me!

**********  **********

Knock Knock
Whos there ?
lettace
lettece who?
lettace in it's cold ot here!!

**********  **********

Q: What is black, white and red?
A: A newspaper!

**********  **********

Q: What's the worse weather for mice?
A: When it's raining cats and dogs.

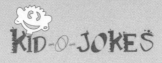

KID-O-JOKES

TEACHER: Tommy, why do you always get so dirty?
TOMMY: Well, I'm a lot closer to the ground
then you are.

*********  **********

Knock Knock
Whos there ?
Mickey
Mickey who?
My key is lost, let me in!!

********* **********

Knock Knock
who's there?
cargo
cargo who?
cargo beep beep and run over the easter bunny

********* **********

Q: What do you call a boomerang that doesn't
come back?
A: A stick!

KID-O-JOKES

TEACHER: Why are you late?
WEBSTER: Because of the sign.
TEACHER: What sign?
WEBSTER: The one that says,
"School Ahead, Go Slow."

********** 🙂 **********

Knock Knock
Whos There?
Ya
Ya who?
What are you getting so excited about?

********** 🙂 **********

Q: Why does a dog turn around 3 times
before lying down?
A: Because one good turn deserves another.

********** 🙂 **********

Q: Why did Donald Duck go to college?
A: He wanted to be a wise quacker!

KID-O-JOKES

SILVIA: Dad, can you write in the dark?
FATHER: I think so. What do you want me to write?
SYLVIA: Your name on this report card.

*********  **********

Knock Knock
Whos there ?
yoo
yoo who?
yoo hoo to you too!

*********  **********

Knock Knock
who's there?
boo
boo who?
don't cry all easter bunny's be back next year.

********* **********

Q: What do you get when you cross a snake
and a kangaroo?
A: A jump rope!

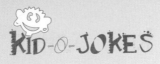

KID-O-JOKES

TEACHER: In this box, I have a 10-foot snake.
SAMMY: You can't fool me,
Teacher... snakes don't have feet.

*********  *********

Knock Knock
Whos there ?
Police
Police who?
Police open the door, I'm Freezing

*********  *********

knock knock
Whos there?
Sarah
Sarah who?
Sarah ghost in the house?

********* *********

Q: Why did the boy bring a ladder to school?
A: He wanted to see what High School was like!

KID-O-JOKES

TEACHER: How can you prevent diseases
caused by biting insects?
JOSE: Don't bite any.

********** 😊 **********

Knock Knock
Whos there ?
Azur
Azur who?
Azur sure love you

********* 😊 **********

Knock knock
Whos there?
Beef
Beef who?
Beef-ore I tell you, let me come in

********* 😊 **********

Q: How do you make a tissue dance?
A: Put a little boogey in it!

TEACHER: Ellen, give me a sentence starting with "I".
ELLEN: I is...
TEACHER: No, Ellen. Always say, "I am."
ELLEN: All right... "I am the ninth letter
of the alphabet."

*********  *********

Knock Knock
Whos there ?
Rhino
Rhino who?
Rhino so many knock-knock jokes, it's ridiculous!

********* :) *********

Q: Why did the Dalmatian have spots?
A: Because they got muddy and it dried.

********* :) *********

Q: Where do bees go to the bathroom?
A: At the BP station!

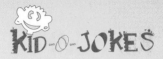

MOTHER: Why on earth did you swallow the money
I gave you?
JUNIOR: You said it was my lunch money.

*********  *********

knock knock
who's there?
cow go
cow go who?
cow don't go who, cow go moo!!!!!!

********* (◡‿◡) *********

knock knock
whos there?
Heaven
Heaven who?
Heaven you heard enough of these knock knock jokes??

********* (◡‿◡) *********

Q: Why does it get hot after a baseball game?
A: Because all the fans have left!

KID-O-JOKES

TEACHER: If I had seven oranges in one hand and
eight oranges in the other, what would I have?
CLASS COMEDIAN: Big hands

*********  **********

Knock Knock
Who is there?
pencil
Pencil who?
Pencil fall down if you don't wear a belt!!!!

********* 😊 **********

Knock, knock
Who's there?
Ach
Ach Who?
God Bless You!

********* 😊 **********

Q: Why did the cookie go to see the doctor?
A: He was feeling crummy!

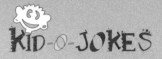

KID-O-JOKES

There was this girl who had brown hair and this guy said,
"What a color, where did you get it?" She said,
"Oh well, it's natural."
Then a girl with blonde hair came in. He said,
"Oh well, well, looking good. What's the secret?"
"It's natural." Then a girl with green hair came in.
He said, "Oh, oh, what on earth is with the do?"
She said, (snort) "It's natural." and whiffed her
hand through her nose and in her hair.

********* 😊 **********

knock knock
who's there ?
aneeda.
aneeda who ?
I aneeda pencil can you give me one?

********* 😊 **********

Q: How do you catch a squirrel?
A: Climb a tree and act like a nut!

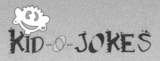

Mum: What are you doing son?
Boy: Writing my brother a letter.
Mum: That's a lovely idea, dear, but why are you
writing so slowly?
Boy: Because he can't read very fast!

*********  *********

knock knock
who's there
venue
venue who
venue going to open the door

*********  *********

Q: How can you tell if a calendar is popular?
A: It has a lot of dates!

*********  *********

Q: Why did the Dalmatian go to the cleaners?
A: His coat had spots all over it.

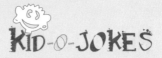

KID-O-JOKES

First Caribou: Ask me if I'm a rabbit.
Second Caribou: Okay. Are you a rabbit?
First Caribou: Yes, I'm a rabbit.
Now ask me if I'm a caribou.
Second Caribou: I'm game, are you a Caribou?
First Caribou: No, silly. I told you I'm a rabbit

*********  **********

Knock-Knock
Who's there?
Justin
Justin who?
Justin time for lunch.

*********  **********

Q: What do pigs put on sore toes?
A: Oinkment!

*********  **********

Q: What key has legs and can't open doors?
A: A Turkey.

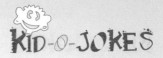

KID-O-JOKES

Two bowling teams charter a double-decker bus;
they're going to Atlantic City for the weekend.
One team is in the bottom of the bus, and
the other team is in the top of the bus.
The team down below is whooping it up when one
of them realizes he doesn't hear anything from the top.
He walks up the stairs, and here are all the
guys from the second team clutching the seats in front
of them with white knuckles, scared to death.
He says, "What the heck's goin' on?
We're down here havin' a grand old time."
One of the guys from the second team says,
"Yeah, but you guys've got a 'driver.'"

*********  **********

Knock knock
Who is there?
Hoo hoo
Hoo hoo who?
Hey! it's not Halloween yet!

********* **********

Q: How do you stop a skunk from smelling?
A: Put a clothes peg on its nose!

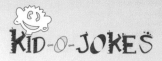

A little kid's in school, taking a true-false test and he's flipping a coin. At the end of the test he's flipping the coin again. The teacher says, "What are you doing?" He says, "Checking my answers."

*********  **********

Knock knock.
Who's there?
Cockadoodle.
Cockadoodle who?
Not cockadoodle who, you silly chicken, cockadoodledoo!

********* :) **********

Knock knock
Whos there
Boo
Boo who
Boo who, what ya cryin about baby.

********* :) **********

Q: When is a car not a car?
A: When it turns into a garage!

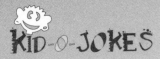
Little Johnny's teacher asked him how the weekend went.
He told her, "Horribly, a car hit my dog in the ass."
She corrected him replying, "rectum." Johnny said,
"Wrecked him? Damn near killed him!!"

********* 😊 **********

knock, knock
whos there?
Ivona
Ivona who?
Ivona tinkle, but i cant find the bathroom

********* 😊 **********

Knock Knock
Who's there
police
police who
police tell me where my jewelry is!

********* 😊 **********

Q: What does a bee use to brush its hair?
A: A honeycomb!

A three-year-old went with his dad to see a litter of kittens.
On returning home, he breathlessly informed his mother
there were 2 boy kittens & 2 girl kittens.
"How did you know?" his mother asked.
"Daddy picked them up and looked underneath,"
he replied, "I think it's printed on the bottom."

********* 🙂 **********

knock knock
who's there?
cargo
Cargo who?
cargo beep beep

********* 🙂 **********

Q: What do you get when you cross a cow with a rabbit?
A: Hare in your milk!

********* 🙂 **********

Q: What fruit teases you a lot?
A: A ba na..na..na..na..na!

KID-O-JOKES

As another three year old put his shoes on by himself.
His mother noticed the left one was on the right foot.
She said, "Son, your shoes are on the wrong feet."
He looked up at her with a raised brow and said,
"Don't kid me, Mom, I know they're my feet."

*********  *********

knock, knock
who's there?
police,
police who?
police to meet you. May I shake your hand?

*********  *********

Q: Why didn't the skeleton cross the road?
A: Because he didnt have the guts!

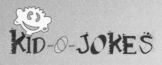

A woodpecker was pecking a hole in the tree.
All of a sudden a flash of lightening struck down the tree.
The woodpecker looked amused for a moment and said,
"Gee, I guess I don't know my own strength!"

*********  **********

knock knock
who's there
Ben
Ben who
Ben knockin on your door all day

********* :) **********

Q: What do you say to a skeleton before he eats?
A: Bone appetit!

********* :) **********

Q: What do you say to a skeleton going on vacation?
A: Bone voyage!

Julie was saying her bedtime prayers.
'Please God,' she said, 'make Naples the
capital of Italy. Make Naples the capital
of Italy-'
Her mother interrupted and said 'Julie, why
do you want God to make Naples the capital
of Italy?'
Julie replied, 'Because that's what I put in
my geography exam!'

*********  *********

Mary: 'I don't think my mother
knows much about children.'
Teacher: 'Why do you say that?'
Mary: 'Because she puts me to
bed when I'm wide awake and gets
me up when I'm sleepy.'

*********  *********

At the scene of a bank robbery
the police sergeant came running
up to his inspector and said,
'He got away,sir!'
The inspector was furious.
'But I told you to put a man on
all the exits!'He roared.
'How could he have got away?'
'He left by one of the entrances, sir!'

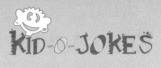

A farmer was showing a schoolboy round his farm
when they came to a field where the farmer's
sheep were grazing.
'How many sheep do you think there are?' Asked the
farmer proudly?
'Seven hundred and sixty four,' replied the boy after
a few minutes.
The farmer gasped. 'That's exactly right, boy.
How did you count them so quickly?'
'Simple,' said the boy genius.'I just counted the legs
and divided by four!'

********** ☺ **********

A man had been unfortunate enough to injure
his hand at work.
As the doctor was examining it he shook his head
and said, 'i'm afraid it'll never be right.'
'Why not doctor?' asked the patient anxiously.
'Because it's your left hand,' replied the doctor.

This edition published in 2010 by

$\mathcal{W}ilco$

Publishing House
Mumbai 400 023. India
Tel: 22041420 / 22842574 Fax: (91-22) 22041429
E mail: wilcos@vsnl.com

ISBN 978-81-88280-81-X

Printed in India

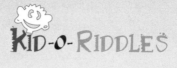

KID-O-RIDDLES

He has a look of awful scorn,
And wears his clothes a funny way,
Waving his hands over fields of corn,
He keeps the birds away!

********?**********

It goes through an apple,
It points out the way,
It fits in a bow,
Then a target, to stay.

********?**********

Here on Earth it's always true,
That a day follows a day.
But there is a place where yesterday
Always follows today!

answers on page 61

3

They can trickle down,
They can tickle too.
Or make you sneeze,
Or comfort you.
Their rustling sound,
You've rarely heard,
Unless you're a pillow
Or a bird!

*********?**********

What has hands,
But is not flesh,
Bone or blood?

*********?**********

The more you take
The more you leave behind.

answers on page 61

4

I am always hungry,
I must always be fed,
The fingers I lick,
Will soon turn red?

********?**********

Take one out and scratch my head
I am now black but once was red.

********?**********

I'm in a rock, not in a stone
I'm in marrow, not in bone
I'm in a bolster, not in a bed
I'm not living, I'm not dead.

answers on page 61

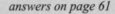

The man who invented it, doesn't want it.
The man who bought it, doesn't need it.
The man who needs it, doesn't know it.

********?**********

What's the beginning of eternity,
The end of time and space,
The beginning of the end,
And the end of every place?

********?**********

They come at night
Without being called
And are lost in the day
Without being stolen.

answers on page 61

There was a green round house.
Inside the green round house
Was a smaller white house.
In the white house was a red house.
In the white house was a red house.
And living in the red house were
Lots of little black babies.

*********?**********

They are dark,
And always on the run.
Without the sun,
There would be none.

*********?**********

What kind of room
Has no windows or doors?

answers on page 61

7

KID-O-RIDDLES

I have holes on the top and bottom.
I have holes on my left and right.
And I have holes in the middle,
Still I hold water.
What am I?

*********?**********

I look at you, you look at me
I raise my right, you raise your left
What is this object?

********?**********

A word I know,
Six letters it contains,
Subtract just one,
And twelve is what remains.

answers on page 61

8

It has no top or bottom
But it can hold flesh, bones and blood
All at the same time.
What is this object?

********* **?** *********

Light as a feather,
There is nothing in it;
The strongest man can't hold it
For much more than a minute?

********* **?** *********

Forward I am heavy,
Backward I am not.
What am I?

answers on page 61

9

It's as big as an apple
But an apple it's not.
Leave it too long,
It surely will rot.
It is sweet when it gives
Your mouth a visit.
Yes, it's a fruit,
But what is it?

*********?**********

What two words have the most letters in it?

*********?**********

What grows in winter
Dies in summer
And has roots that grow up?

answers on page 61

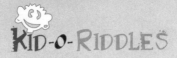
What can run but never walks,
Has a mouth but never talks,
Has a head but never weeps,
Has a bed but never sleeps?

*********?**********

What common English verb becomes
Its own past tense by rearranging its letters?

*********?**********

Yellow and white
Hard outside
Stolen from life
What am I?

answers on page 61

11

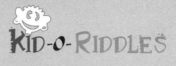

What five letter English word
Does not change its pronunciation
When four letters are taken away?

*********?**********

When is a door not a door?

*********?**********

Until I am measured,
I am not known,
Yet how you miss me
When I have flown?

*********?**********

The more there is the less you see.

answers on page 61

Kid-o-Riddles

As I walked along the path
I saw something with four fingers
And one thumb,
But it was not flesh, fish, bone or fowl.

*********?**********

What occurs once in a minute,
Twice in a moment,
But never in an hour.

*********?**********

Though it is not an ox,
It has horns;
Though it is not an ass,
It has a pack-saddle;
And wherever it goes
It leaves silver behind.

answers on page 61

13

KID-O-RIDDLES

I have a 100 legs but cannot stand.
A long neck but no head.
And I eat the maids life.

*********?**********

I run, yet I have no legs. What am I?

*********?**********

What is black and white and is 'red' all over?

*********?**********

It goes up and down the stairs
Without moving.

answers on page 61

14

KID-O-RIDDLES

What eats rocks,
Levels mountains,
Rusts metal,
Pushes the clouds across the sky,
And can make a young man old?

********* ? *********

What gets wetter the more it dries?

********* ? *********

Who are the two brothers
Who live on opposite sides of the road
Yet never see each other?

answers on page 61

15

KID-O-RIDDLES

What object has keys
That open no locks,
Space but no room,
And you can enter but
Not go in?

********?**********

What can you catch but not throw?

********?**********

Use me well and I am everybody,
Scratch my back and I am nobody.

answers on page 61

KID-O-RIDDLES

I went into the woods and got it
I sat down to seek it
I brought it home with me
Because I couldn't find it

*********?**********

You use a knife
To slice my head,
And weep beside me
When I am dead.

*********?**********

I have rivers without water,
Forests without trees,
Mountains without rocks
Towns without houses.

answers on page 61

17

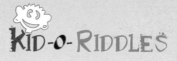

The part of the bird that's not in the sky,
Who can swim in the ocean
And yet remain dry.

***********?************

No sooner spoken than broken.
What is it?

***********?************

I have two heads but only one body,
The more still I stand the faster I run.

***********?************

What one word has the most letters in it?

answers on page 62

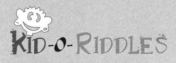

KID-O-RIDDLES

It is weightless,
You can see it
And if you put it in a barrel
It will make the barrel lighter?

********* ? *********

If you throw it off the highest building
It will not break.
If you place it in the ocean
It will.

********* ? *********

In many hallways you would stand,
If not with this in hand.

answers on page 62

19

KID-O-RIDDLES

The rich men want it,
The wise men know it,
The poor all need it,
And the kind men show it.

*********?*********

Squeeze it and it cries tears
As red as its flesh,
But its heart is made of stone.

*********?*********

If you have it,
You want to share it.
If you share it,
You don't have it.

answers on page 62

20

What we caught
We threw away,
What we didn't catch
We kept.

*********?**********

I am the black child of a white father,
A wingless bird,
Flying even to the clouds of heaven.
I give birth to tears of mourning
In pupils that meet me,
Even though there is no cause for grief,
And at once on my birth I am dissolved into air.

*********?**********

What goes round the house
And in the house
But never touches the house?

answers on page 62

21

KID-O-RIDDLES

I am both Mother and Father.
I am seldom still
Yet I never wander.
I never birth nor nurse.

*********?**********

I am taken from a mine,
And shut up in a wooden case,
From which I am never released,
And yet I am used by almost everybody.

*********?**********

What is it that you can keep
After giving it to someone else?

answers on page 62

22

Born Motherless and Fatherless,
Into this world without a sin
Made a loud roar as I entered
And never spoke again.

*********?**********

What walks all day on its head?

*********?**********

There is a thing that nothing is,
And yet it has a name.
It's sometimes tall and sometimes short,
Joins our talks and joins our sports,
And plays at every game?

answers on page 62

Through wind and rain I always play,
I roam the earth, yet here I stay;
I crumble stones, and fire cannot burn me;
Yet I am soft
You can gauge me with your hand.

*********?*********

What is round as a dishpan,
Deep as a tub,
And still the oceans couldn't fill it up?

*********?*********

It is more beautiful than the face of your love.
It is more scary than your worst fear.
Dead men eat it all the time.
If a live man eats it, he soon will die.
A poor man has it.
A rich man wants it.

answers on page 62

24

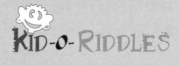

KID-O-RIDDLES

A little pool with two layers of wall around it.
One white and soft and the other dark and hard,
Amidst a light brown grassy lawn
With an outline of a green grass.

*********?*********

Who spends the day at the window,
Goes to the table for meals
And hides at night?

*********?*********

I bind it and it walks.
I loose it and it stops.

answers on page 62

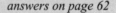

25

KID-O-RIDDLES

He who has it doesn't tell it.
He who takes it doesn't know it.
He who knows it doesn't want it.
What is it?

********?**********

What goes round and round the wood
But never goes into the wood?

********?**********

You peel the outside,
Boil the inside,
Nibble on the outside
And throw the inside in
The garbage?

answers on page 62

26

KID-O-RIDDLES

Pronounced as one letter,
And written with three,
Two letters there are,
And two only in me.
I'm double, I'm single,
I'm black, blue and grey,
I'm read from both ends,
And the same either way.

*********?**********

It stands on one leg
With its heart in its head.

*********?**********

It's been around for millions of years,
But it's no more than a month old.
What is it?

answers on page 62

27

KID-O-RIDDLES

What breaks but never falls
And what falls but
Never breaks?

*********?**********

What keeps the moon
From falling?

*********?**********

What belongs to you
But others use it more than you do?

answers on page 62

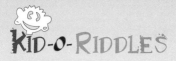

We are little creatures;
All of us have different features.
One of us in glass is set;
One of us you'll find in jet.
Another you may see in tin,
And the fourth is boxed within,
If the fifth you should pursue,
It can never fly from you.
What are we?

********* **?** *********

What dog has no tail?

********* **?** *********

What is faster than the speed of sound,
But is still human?

answers on page 62

KID-O-RIDDLES

A hole leading in,
A hole leading out,
We connect to a cavern
That is slimy all throughout.
What are we?

*********?**********

I'm the source of all emotion,
But I'm caged in a white prison.

*********?**********

Rain is spent.
Now colors bent
Frame a clear, blue sky.

answers on page 62

30

I can kill people but without me
There would be no people.
I was born long ago
And will someday die.
I can cause fire and
Am a magician with water.
I have more brothers than any person.
There is very little that can stop me.

*********?*********

What goes into the water black
And comes out red?

*********?*********

When one does not know what it is,
Then it is something;
But when one knows what it is,
Then it is nothing.

answers on page 62

KID-O-RIDDLES

The wind, it blows my house around.
And worms, I pluck them from the ground.
A song, I sing it sweet and clear,
And wings, they fly when cats come near.

*********?**********

Come follow me though I can't move.
Still, I will lead you through the trees.
Come follow me though I've no voice
To call you on the breeze.
These woods are wild as they can be.
I know them well.
Come, follow me.

*********?**********

What is round on the ends
And high in the middle?.

answers on page 63

32

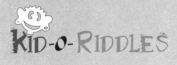

KID-O-RIDDLES

I look like a bee all black and yellow
But I'm a wiggly, squiggly fellow,
Munching milkweed at all hours.
Someday, I will dine on flowers.
Then I won't be a wiggly guy.
I'll have wings to fly, fly, fly.

*********?**********

I bury bones and bark at cars
And sometimes howl
Beneath the stars.
I like to eat, and love to play,
Not like cats who sleep all day.

*********?**********

What is it that you will break
Even when you name it?

answers on page 63

33

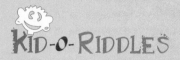

From end to end I span the air,
So you can go from here to there
I land on land, though I've no wings.
I'm made of much more solid things.

* * * * * * * * * ? * * * * * * * * * *

Almost everyone sees me without noticing me,
For what is beyond is what they seek.

* * * * * * * * * ? * * * * * * * * * *

As I went across the bridge,
I met a man with a load of wood
Which was neither straight nor crooked.
What kind of wood was it?

answers on page 63

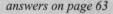

34

KID-O-RIDDLES

I can be created by humans,
But they cannot control me.
I suck on wood, paper and flesh alike.
I can be more of a hindrance
Than a help at times.
To my creators, I seem to be everywhere at once.

*********?**********

What is it
That men do standing up,
Ladies do sitting down
And dogs do on three legs?

*********?**********

What is put on a table,
Cut, but never eaten?

answers on page 63

35

KID-O-RIDDLES

I am the fountain from which no one can drink.
For many I am considered a necessary link.
Like gold to all I am sought for,
But my continued death brings wealth
For all to want more.

*********?*********

What can you put
In a wooden box,
That will make it lighter?

*********?*********

What kind of can
Never needs a can-opener?

answers on page 63

36

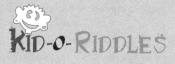

KID-O-RIDDLES

I have a little house in which I live all alone,
It has no doors or windows,
And if I want to go out
I must break through the wall.

*********?**********

There are four brothers in this world
That were all born together.
The first runs and never wearies.
The second eats and is never full.
The third drinks and is always thirsty.
The fourth sings a song that is never good.

*********?**********

A cowboy rode to an inn on Friday.
He stayed two nights
And left on Friday.
How could that be?

answers on page 63

Kid-o-Riddles

A cloud was my mother,
The wind is my father,
My son is the cool stream,
And my daughter
Is the fruit of the land.
A rainbow is my bed,
The earth my final resting place,
And I'm the torment of man.

*********?**********

Poke your fingers in my eyes
And I will open wide my jaws.
Linen cloth, quills, or paper,
My greedy lust devours them all.

*********?**********

What doesn't get any wetter,
No matter how much it rains?

answers on page 63

38

KID-O-RIDDLES

I am the beginning of sorrow,
And the end of sickness.
You cannot express happiness
Without me,
Yet I am in the midst of crosses.
I am always in risk,
Yet never in danger.
You may find me in the sun,
But I am never out of darkness.

********** ? **********

In the day or in the night
All people have seen this sight,
On the ocean or on the plain
Most people have seen the same,
On this world and on no other
Has been shown to me by my brother,
Some leader once generalized it
But many things have been called it.

answers on page 63

KID-O-RIDDLES

Here is one that has a head without an eye,
And there's one that has an eye without a head.
You may find the answer if you try;
And when all is said,
Half the answer hangs by a thread.

*********?*********

Black I am and much admired,
Men seek me until they're tired;
When they find me, break my head,
And take me from my resting bed.

*********?*********

What runs around a city
But never moves?

answers on page 63

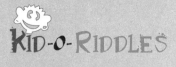

KID-O-RIDDLES

Iron roof, glass walls
Burns and burns
And never falls.

********?**********

I cut through evil
Like a double edged sword,
And chaos flees at my approach.
Balance I single-handedly upraise,
Through battles fought with heart and mind,
Instead of with my gaze.

********?**********

A box without hinges, key, or lid,
Yet golden treasure inside is hid.

answers on page 63

41

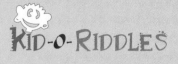

KID-O-RIDDLES

It cannot be seen, cannot be felt,
Cannot be heard, cannot be smelt.
It lies behind stars and under hills,
And empty holes it fills.
It comes first and follows after,
Ends life, kills laughter.

*********?**********

This thing all things devours:
Birds, beast, trees, flowers;
Gnaws iron, bites steel;
Grinds hard stones to meal;
Slays king, ruins town,
And beats high mountains down.

*********?**********

What kind of ear cannot hear?

answers on page 63

42

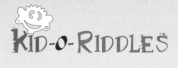

KID-O-RIDDLES

If you break me
I do not stop working,
If you touch me
I may be snared,
If you lose me
Nothing will matter.

********* **?** **********

My life can be measured in hours,
I serve by being devoured.
Thin, I am quick
Fat, I am slow
Wind is my foe.

********* **?** **********

What fastens two people
Yet touches only one?

answers on page 63

43

 KID-O-RIDDLES

I am always hungry,
I must always be fed,
The finger I lick
Will soon turn red.

*********?**********

Voiceless cries,
Wingless flutters,
Toothless bites,
Mouthless mutters.

*********?**********

Thirty white horses on a red hill,
First they champ,
Then they stamp,
Then they stand still.

answers on page 63

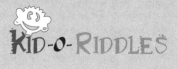

KID-O-RIDDLES

They have not flesh, nor feathers,
Nor scales, nor bone.
Yet they have fingers and thumbs,
Of their own.

*********?**********

I weaken all men for hours each day.
I show you strange visions while you are away.
I take you by night, by day take you back,
None suffer to have me, but do from my lack.

*********?**********

I make you weak at the worst of all times.
I keep you safe, I keep you fine.
I make your hands sweat,
And your heart grow cold,
I visit the weak,
But seldom the bold.

answers on page 63

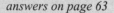

45

KID-O-RIDDLES

You're a bus driver.
At the first stop 4 people get on.
At the second stop 8 people get on,
At the third stop 2 people get off,
At the fourth stop everyone got off.
What color are the bus drivers eyes?

*********?**********

A man went outside in the pouring rain,
With no protection,
But not a hair on his head got wet...
How come?

*********?**********

I am as strong as seven men.
I am as tall as seven men.
Yet seven men can not
Stand me on my end.

answers on page 63

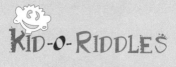

KID-O-RIDDLES

If a cat can jump 5 feet high,
Then why can't it jump through
A 3 foot high window?

* * * * * * * * * ? * * * * * * * * * *

Twelve pears hanging high,
Twelve men passing by,
Each took a pear
And left eleven hanging there.
How can this be?

* * * * * * * * * ? * * * * * * * * * *

Two brothers we are, great burden we bear
By which we are bitterly pressed.
In truth we may say
We are full all the day
But empty we go to our rest.

answers on page 64

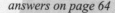

47

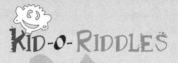

KID-O-RIDDLES

You are stuck in a dungeon
With one match in your hand.
The only other things in the room
Are a newspaper, a fire,
And an oil lamp.
Which do you light first?

*********?**********

In the dark night flies a many-hued phantom.
It soars and spreads its wings
Above the gloomy human crowd.
The whole world calls to it,
The whole world implores it.
At dawn the phantom vanishes
To be reborn in every heart.
And every night it is born anew
And every day it dies!

answers on page 64

KID-O-RIDDLES

What would you call 5 bottles
Of fizzy lemonade?

*********?**********

Why doea a horse have
6 legs?

*********?**********

What do you call 2 banana peels?

*********?**********

What does the winner of a
Running race always loose?

answers on page 64

49

KID-O-RIDDLES

What goes around the world
And stays in a corner?

***********?************

Give it food and it will live;
Give it water and it will die.

***********?************

A white dove flew down by the castle.
Along came a king and picked it up handless,
Ate it up toothless,
And carried it away wingless.

***********?************

Where does a bird go when it loses its tail?

answers on page 64

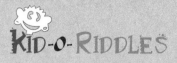

Only two backbones, a thousand ribs.

*********?*********

Brothers and sisters have I none
but that man's father is my father's son.

*********?*********

Lives without a body,
Hears without ears,
Speaks without a mouth,
To which the air alone gives birth.

*********?*********

What can fill a room
But takes up no space.

answers on page 64

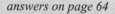

KID-O-RIDDLES

Lighter than what
I am made of,
More of me is hidden
Than is seen.

*********?**********

I go around in circles,
But always straight ahead
Never complain,
No matter where I am led.

*********?**********

How can you place a pencil on the floor
So that no one can jump over it ?

answers on page 64

52

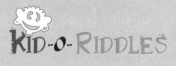

If Washington's wife
Washed Washington's clothes
While watching TV.
How many "W"s in all?

*********?**********

What is that which goes with a carriage,
Comes with a carriage,
Is of no use to a carriage,
And yet the carriage cannot go without it?

*********?**********

Where will you always,
Find diamonds?

answers on page 64

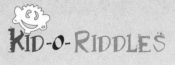
What wears a coat all winter
And pants in the winter?

********?**********

Ten Men's Strength,
Ten Men's Length,
Ten Men can't break it,
Yet a young boy walks off with it

********?**********

What goes up the chimney down,
But can't go down the chimney up?

answers on page 64

54

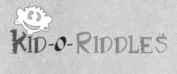

KID-O-RIDDLES

I begin eternity,
And end space,
At the end of time,
And in every place,
Last in life,
Second to death,
Never alone,
Found in your breath,
Contained by earth,
Water or flame,
My grandeur so awesome,
Wind dare not tame,
Not in your mind,
Am in your dreams,
Vacant to Kings,
Present to Queens.

*********?**********

What driver doesn't have a license?

answers on page 64

55

KID-O-RIDDLES

I have many tongues but cannot taste
By me, most things are turned to waste
I crack and snap, yet I stay whole
I may take the largest toll
I assisted all of the first men
And I will pay them back again
Around me, people snuggle and sleep
Yet run when I am released from my keep
I jump around and leap and bound
The cold man wishes I he had found

*********?**********

What is the longest word in the
English language?

*********?**********

Why do statues and paintings of
George Washington always show him standing?

answers on page 64

56

KID-O-RIDDLES

I turn my head and you may go where you want.
I turn it again, you will stay till you rot.
I have no face, but I live or die
By my crooked teeth

*********?**********

What is the brightest fish?

*********?**********

What has a neck, but no head?

*********?**********

What pillar is never used
To hold up a building?

answers on page 64

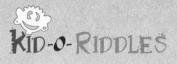

Why doesn't the sea ever
Fall into space?

*********?**********

Why is there always a
Wall around a graveyard?

*********?**********

It holds most knowledge that has ever been said;
But is not the brain, is not the head.
To feathers and their masters,
'Tis both bane and boon. . .
One empty, and one full.

answers on page 64

KID-O-RIDDLES

A commonly used word
That ends in T
Contains the letter VEN
And starts with IN?

*********?**********

What is small and round and has holes?

*********?**********

So fragile that even
Saying its name
Can break it?

answers on page 64

59

KID-O-RIDDLES

What has the fur of a Cat,
The whiskers of a Cat,
The ears of Cat,
The tail of a Cat,
But is not a cat?

*********?**********

What lies at the bottom
Of the sea and shivers?

*********?**********

Starts with 'T'
Ends with 'T'
And is full of 'T'?

answers on page 64

60

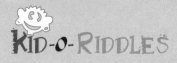

KID-O-RIDDLES

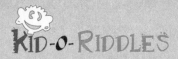
KID-O-RIDDLES

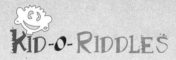

KID-O-RIDDLES

Page 32
a) A BIRD!!
b) A PATH!!
c) The word OHIO = O-HI-O!!
Page 33
a) A CATERPILLAR!!
b) A DOG!!
c) SILENCE!!
Page 34
a) A BRIDGE!!
b) A WINDOW!!
c) SAWDUST!!
Page 35
a) A BABY!!
b) SHAKE HANDS!!
c) A pack of CARDS!!
Page 36
a) OIL!!
b) HOLES!!
c) A PELICAN!!
Page 37
a) A CHICKEN in an EGG!!
b) WATER, FIRE, EARTH, WIND!!
c) His Horse's NAME was FRIDAY.
Page 38
a) RAIN!!
b) SHEARS or SCISSORS!!
c) The OCEAN!!

Page 39
a) The letter "S"!!
b) A MONSTER!!
Page 40
a) PINS AND NEEDLES!!
b) COAL!!
c) A WALL!!
Page 41
a) A LANTERN!!
b) JUSTICE!!
c) EGG!!
Page 42
a) DARKNESS!!
b) TIME!!
c) An ear of CORN!!
Page 43
a) HOPE!!
b) CANDLE!!
c) A WEDDING RING!!
Page 44
a) FIRE!!
b) WIND!!
c) TEETH!!
Page 45
a) GLOVES!!
b) SLEEP!!
c) FEAR!!
Page 46
a) SAME COLOR AS YOURS!!
(you are the bus driver)
b) He is BALD!!
c) A ROPE!!

Page 47
a) The window is CLOSED!!
b) "Each" is a man's NAME!!
c) SHOES or BOOTS!!

Page 48
a) The MATCH!!
b) HOPE or DREAMS!!

Page 49
a) A POP-GROUP!!
b) Cause it has FORLEGS in front and 2 behind!!
c) A pair of SLIPPERS!!
d) His BREATH!!

Page 50
a) A STAMP!!
b) FIRE!!
c) SNOW MELTED by the SUN!!
d) The RETAIL STORE!!

Page 51
a) RAILROAD!!
b) My SON!!
c) An ECHO!!
d) LIGHT!!

Page 52
a) ICE!!
b) WHEEL!!
c) Put it NEXT to the WALL!!

Page 53
a) NONE, there are no "W"s in "ALL"!!
b) NOISE!!
c) In a pack of CARDS!!

Page 54
a) A DOG!!
b) A ROPE!!
c) An UMBRELLA!!

Page 55
a) The letter "E"!!
b) A SCREW DRIVER!!

Page 56
a) FIRE!!
b) SMILES!! (there is a mile in between
c) Because he would NEVER LIE!!

Page 57
a) A KEY!!
b) A SUN FISH!!
c) A BOTTLE!!
d) A CATERPILLAR!!

Page 58
a) Its TIDE!!
b) Because people are just DYING to get in!!
c) PAPER!!

Page 59
a) INVENT!!
b) A BUTTON!!
c) SILENCE

Page 60
a) A KITTEN!!
b) A NERVOUS WRECK!!
c) A TEAPOT!!